Maid of Honor

WEDDING DUTIES
PLANNER

ISBN # 978-0-578-38777-2

Beauty and Heart Planners

P.O. Box 6711

Los Osos, California 93422

Table of CONTENTS

12-Month Undated
CALENDARS

January

MON	TUE	WED	THU	FRI	SAT	SUN

NOTES

February

MON	TUE	WED	THU	FRI	SAT	SUN

NOTES

March

MON	TUE	WED	THU	FRI	SAT	SUN

NOTES

April

MON	TUE	WED	THU	FRI	SAT	SUN

NOTES

May

MON	TUE	WED	THU	FRI	SAT	SUN

NOTES

June

MON	TUE	WED	THU	FRI	SAT	SUN

NOTES

July

MON	TUE	WED	THU	FRI	SAT	SUN

NOTES

August

MON	TUE	WED	THU	FRI	SAT	SUN

NOTES

September

MON	TUE	WED	THU	FRI	SAT	SUN

NOTES

October

MON	TUE	WED	THU	FRI	SAT	SUN

NOTES

November

MON	TUE	WED	THU	FRI	SAT	SUN

NOTES

December

MON	TUE	WED	THU	FRI	SAT	SUN

NOTES

Maid of Honor Duties

CHECKLISTS

— ♥ —

Maid of Honor Duties CHECKLIST

12-18 MONTHS BEFORE THE WEDDING

- [ ] Help the bride shop for a wedding dress
- [ ] Help shop for bridesmaid dresses
- [ ] Help look for vendors
- [ ]
- [ ]
- [ ]
- [ ]

NOTES

3-6 MONTHS BEFORE THE WEDDING

- [ ] Start planning bachelorette/bridal party
- [ ] Consult with bridesmaids
- [ ] Coordinate hair, makeup, etc...
- [ ]
- [ ]
- [ ]
- [ ]

NOTES

2-3 MONTHS BEFORE THE WEDDING

- [ ] Shop for a wedding gift
- [ ] Schedule alteration appointments
- [ ] Book hair and make up appointments
- [ ] Put together the wedding day kit
- [ ]
- [ ]
- [ ]

NOTES

Maid of Honor Duties CHECKLIST

1 MONTH BEFORE THE WEDDING

- [ ] Write toast for wedding day
- [ ] Finalize your accessories/hair style/other
- [ ] Share about the wedding registry
- [ ] Host a bridal shower
- [ ]
- [ ]
- [ ]

NOTES

SHORTLY BEFORE THE WEDDING

- [ ] Keep bridesmaids up-to-date on plans
- [ ] Host a bachelorette party
- [ ]
- [ ]
- [ ]
- [ ]
- [ ]

NOTES

WEDDING DAY

- [ ] Help the bride get ready
- [ ] Hold bride's bouquet during ceremony
- [ ] Offer support throughout the day!
- [ ]
- [ ]
- [ ]
- [ ]

NOTES

Maid of Honor Duties CHECKLIST

12-18 MONTHS BEFORE THE WEDDING

- [ ]
- [ ]
- [ ]
- [ ]
- [ ]
- [ ]

NOTES

3-6 MONTHS BEFORE THE WEDDING

- [ ]
- [ ]
- [ ]
- [ ]
- [ ]
- [ ]

NOTES

2-3 MONTHS BEFORE THE WEDDING

- [ ]
- [ ]
- [ ]
- [ ]
- [ ]
- [ ]

NOTES

Maid of Honor Duties CHECKLIST

1 MONTH BEFORE THE WEDDING	NOTES
☐	
☐	
☐	
☐	
☐	
☐	

SHORTLY BEFORE THE WEDDING	NOTES
☐	
☐	
☐	
☐	
☐	

WEDDING DAY	NOTES
☐	
☐	
☐	
☐	
☐	
☐	

Notes

Notes

—— ♥ ——

Wedding Day Budget TRACKER

ITEM	BUDGET	ACTUAL	NOTES

Wedding Day Budget TRACKER

ITEM	BUDGET	ACTUAL	NOTES

Notes

_ ❤ _

Bridal Shower Budget TRACKER

ITEM	BUDGET	ACTUAL	NOTES

Bridal Shower Budget TRACKER

ITEM	BUDGET	ACTUAL	NOTES

Notes

Bachelorette Budget TRACKER

ITEM	BUDGET	ACTUAL	NOTES

Bachelorette Budget TRACKER

ITEM	BUDGET	ACTUAL	NOTES

Notes

— ❤ —

Wedding Attire

DETAILS

—— ♥ ——

Wedding Attire IDEAS

HELP THE BRIDE SHOP - POSSIBLE BRIDESMAID DRESS VENDORS

VENDOR	APPOINTMENT	ADDRESS	PHONE

POSSIBLE BRIDAL GOWN VENDORS

VENDOR	APPOINTMENT	ADDRESS	PHONE

Dress & Accessory DETAILS

BRIDAL SHOP INFORMATION

AME & PHONE	
ADDRESS	
WEBSITE	

FITTING APPOINTMENTS

FIRST FITTING	
SECOND FITTING	
FINAL FITTING	

MAID OF HONOR ATTIRE

DRESS SIZE		DRESS COLOR	
DESIGNER		SHOE SIZE	
YLE NUMBER		SHOE STYLE	

MAID OF HONOR HAIR & ACCESSORIES

NAILS		ACCESSORIES
HAIR STYLE		**HAIR / NAIL SALON APPOINTMENT DETAILS**
JEWELRY		

OTHER IMPORTANT DETAILS & CHECKLIST

				REMINDERS
☐	DRESS ORDERED	☐	ACCESSORIES ORDERED	
☐	DRESS ARRIVED	☐	ACCESSORIES ARRIVED	
☐	DRESS TAILORED	☐		
☐	DRESS FINISHED	☐		
☐	SHOES ORDERED	☐		
☐	SHOES ARRIVED	☐		

NOTES

Ideas

WRITE DOWN YOUR THOUGHTS AND IDEAS FOR WEDDING ATTIRE, ETC...

Ideas

WRITE DOWN YOUR THOUGHTS AND IDEAS FOR WEDDING ATTIRE, ETC...

Notes

— ♥ —

Wedding Day
TIMELINE

— ♥ —

Wedding Day TIMELINE

DATE	TIME	DESCRIPTION	NOTES

Wedding Day
KIT

Wedding Day KIT

MAKEUP TOUCH UPS

- [ ] Concealer
- [ ] Bronzer
- [ ] Highlighter
- [ ] Powder
- [ ] Eyeshadow
- [ ] Eyeliner
- [ ] Lipstick
- [ ] Lip balm
- [ ] Compact Mirror
- [ ] Tweezers
- [ ] Nail File
- [ ]
- [ ]
- [ ]
- [ ]
- [ ]
- [ ]
- [ ]

HAIR TOUCH UPS

- [ ] Hairspray
- [ ] Bobby pins
- [ ] Hair clips/ties
- [ ] Brush
- [ ] Curling Iron
- [ ] Straightener
- [ ]
- [ ]
- [ ]
- [ ]
- [ ]
- [ ]
- [ ]
- [ ]
- [ ]
- [ ]
- [ ]
- [ ]

WARDROBE TOUCH UPS

- [ ] Sewing Kit
- [ ] Lint Roller
- [ ] Safety Pins
- [ ] Small Scissors
- [ ]
- [ ]
- [ ]
- [ ]
- [ ]
- [ ]
- [ ]
- [ ]
- [ ]
- [ ]
- [ ]
- [ ]

NOTES

NOTES

NOTES

Wedding Day KIT

FRESHENING UP	MEDICAL NEEDS	OTHER
☐ Mouthwash	☐ Advil or Tylenol	☐ Phone charger
☐ Toothpaste/Toothbrush	☐ Antacid	☐ Cash
☐ Mints	☐ Band-Aids	☐ Hand sanitizer
☐ Chewing gum	☐ Sunscreen	☐
☐ Deodorant	☐	☐
☐ Perfume	☐	☐
☐ Tissue/Kleenex	☐	☐
☐	☐	☐
☐	☐	☐
☐	☐	☐
☐	☐	☐
☐	☐	☐
☐	☐	☐
☐	☐	☐
☐	☐	☐
☐	☐	☐
☐	☐	☐
☐	☐	☐

NOTES	NOTES	NOTES

Wedding Day KIT

MAKEUP TOUCH UPS	HAIR TOUCH UPS	WARDROBE
☐	☐	☐
☐	☐	☐
☐	☐	☐
☐	☐	☐
☐	☐	☐
☐	☐	☐
☐	☐	☐
☐	☐	☐
☐	☐	☐
☐	☐	☐
☐	☐	☐
☐	☐	☐
☐	☐	☐
☐	☐	☐
☐	☐	☐
☐	☐	☐
☐	☐	☐
☐	☐	☐

NOTES	NOTES	NOTES

Wedding Day KIT

FOR FRESHENING UP	FOR MEDICAL NEEDS	OTHER
☐	☐	☐
☐	☐	☐
☐	☐	☐
☐	☐	☐
☐	☐	☐
☐	☐	☐
☐	☐	☐
☐	☐	☐
☐	☐	☐
☐	☐	☐
☐	☐	☐
☐	☐	☐
☐	☐	☐
☐	☐	☐
☐	☐	☐
☐	☐	☐
☐	☐	☐
☐	☐	☐

NOTES	NOTES	NOTES

Wedding-Ready BEAUTY

HAIR

HAIR STYLE	
SALON NAME	
STYLIST NAME	
STYLE IDEAS	
DEPOSIT	
TOTAL COST	

MAKEUP

SALON	
MAKEUP ARTIST	
ADDRESS	
CONSULTATION	
DEPOSIT	
TOTAL COST	

NAILS

SALON	
CONTACT	
STYLE	
CONSULTATION	
DEPOSIT	
TOTAL COST	

SPA/OTHER

DAY OF WEDDING APPOINTMENT TIMES

HAIR:	NAILS:	MAKEUP:

NOTES

Ideas

WRITE DOWN YOUR THOUGHTS AND IDEAS FOR BEAUTY, HAIR, MAKEUP, ETC...

Ideas

WRITE DOWN YOUR THOUGHTS AND IDEAS FOR BEAUTY, HAIR, MAKEUP, ETC...

Notes

—— ♥ ——

Wedding Toast
PLANNER

— ♥ —

Wedding Day TOAST

Toast to the New COUPLE

Toast to the New COUPLE

Notes

Bridal Party

CONTACTS

— ♥ —

Bridal Party CONTACTS

BRIDE'S PARENTS

CONTACT INFORMATION
📞 PHONE

✉️ EMAIL

GROOM'S PARENTS

CONTACT INFORMATION
📞 PHONE

✉️ EMAIL

BRIDESMAID

CONTACT INFORMATION
📞 PHONE

✉️ EMAIL

BRIDESMAID

CONTACT INFORMATION
📞 PHONE

✉️ EMAIL

BRIDESMAID

CONTACT INFORMATION
📞 PHONE

✉️ EMAIL

BRIDESMAID

CONTACT INFORMATION
📞 PHONE

✉️ EMAIL

BRIDESMAID

CONTACT INFORMATION
📞 PHONE

✉️ EMAIL

BRIDESMAID

CONTACT INFORMATION
📞 PHONE

✉️ EMAIL

BRIDESMAID

CONTACT INFORMATION
📞 PHONE

✉️ EMAIL

Bridal Party CONTACTS

BEST MAN		CONTACT INFORMATION
		PHONE
		EMAIL

GROOMSMAN		CONTACT INFORMATION
		PHONE
		EMAIL

GROOMSMAN		CONTACT INFORMATION
		PHONE
		EMAIL

GROOMSMAN		CONTACT INFORMATION
		PHONE
		EMAIL

GROOMSMAN		CONTACT INFORMATION
		PHONE
		EMAIL

GROOMSMAN		CONTACT INFORMATION
		PHONE
		EMAIL

GROOMSMAN		CONTACT INFORMATION
		PHONE
		EMAIL

GROOMSMAN		CONTACT INFORMATION
		PHONE
		EMAIL

OTHER		CONTACT INFORMATION
		PHONE
		EMAIL

Bridal Party CONTACTS

CONTACT INFORMATION
📞 PHONE
✉ EMAIL

CONTACT INFORMATION
📞 PHONE
✉ EMAIL

CONTACT INFORMATION
📞 PHONE
✉ EMAIL

CONTACT INFORMATION
📞 PHONE
✉ EMAIL

CONTACT INFORMATION
📞 PHONE
✉ EMAIL

CONTACT INFORMATION
📞 PHONE
✉ EMAIL

CONTACT INFORMATION
📞 PHONE
✉ EMAIL

CONTACT INFORMATION
📞 PHONE
✉ EMAIL

CONTACT INFORMATION
📞 PHONE
✉ EMAIL

Vendor
CONTACTS

Vendor CONTACTS

DRESS VENDOR

- 👤 NAME
- ✉️ EMAIL
- 📞 PHON

HAIR STYLIST / SALON

- 👤 NAME
- ✉️ EMAIL
- 📞 PHONE

MAKEUP ARTIST

- 👤 NAME
- ✉️ EMAIL
- 📞 PHONE

TAILOR

- 👤 NAME
- ✉️ EMAIL
- 📞 PHONE

WEDDING PLANNER

- 👤 NAME
- ✉️ EMAIL
- 📞 PHONE

LOCATION OF BRIDAL SHOWER

- 👤 NAME
- ✉️ EMAIL
- 📞 PHONE

NAIL SALON

- 👤 NAME
- ✉️ EMAIL
- 📞 PHONE

OTHER:

- 👤 NAME
- ✉️ EMAIL
- 📞 PHONE

Vendor CONTACTS

NAME

EMAIL

PHONE

NAME

EMAIL

PHONE

NAME

EMAIL

PHONE

NAME

EMAIL

PHONE

NAME

EMAIL

PHONE

NAME

EMAIL

PHONE

NAME

EMAIL

PHONE

NAME

EMAIL

PHONE

Bridal Shower
PLANNER

— ♥ —

Bridal Shower PLANNER

BRIDAL SHOWER DATE

IDEAS, THEME, COLORS	NOTES

VENUE & VENDOR CONTACTS

FOOD & ENTERTAINMENT

NOTES

DELEGATION / TO DO

Ideas

WRITE DOWN YOUR THOUGHTS AND IDEAS FOR THE BRIDAL SHOWER

Ideas

WRITE DOWN YOUR THOUGHTS AND IDEAS FOR THE BRIDAL SHOWER

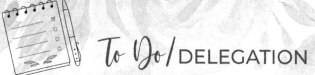

To Do/DELEGATION

NAME / TO DO	NOTES

NAME / TO DO	NOTES

NAME / TO DO	NOTES

To Do/DELEGATION

NAME / TO DO	NOTES

NAME / TO DO	NOTES

NAME / TO DO	NOTES

Bridal Shower GUESTS

NAME & CONTACT	RSVP'D		NAME & CONTACT	RSVP'D	
	✗	✔		✗	✔
	✗	✔		✗	✔
	✗	✔		✗	✔
	✗	✔		✗	✔
	✗	✔		✗	✔
	✗	✔		✗	✔
	✗	✔		✗	✔
	✗	✔		✗	✔
	✗	✔		✗	✔
	✗	✔		✗	✔
	✗	✔		✗	✔
	✗	✔		✗	✔
	✗	✔		✗	✔
	✗	✔		✗	✔
	✗	✔		✗	✔
	✗	✔		✗	✔
	✗	✔		✗	✔
	✗	✔		✗	✔
	✗	✔		✗	✔
	✗	✔		✗	✔
	✗	✔		✗	✔
	✗	✔		✗	✔
	✗	✔		✗	✔

Bridal Shower Gift TRACKER

NAME	GIFT	ADDRESS	NOTES

Bridal Shower Gift TRACKER

NAME	GIFT	ADDRESS	NOTES

Notes

— ♥ —

Bachelorette Party
PLANNER

— ♥ —

Bachelorette Party PLANNER

DATE: **LOCATION:**

4-6 MONTHS BEFORE	3-4 MONTHS BEFORE	REMINDERS

2-4 WEEKS BEFORE

WEEK BEFORE

DAY OF BACHELORETTE PARTY

Bachelorette Party DETAILS

DATE: **START TIME:**

IMPORTANT CONTACTS

TIME	KEY EVENTS	BOOKED

DETAILS

LOCATION NAME

PHONE CONTACT

ADDRESS

NOTES

CHECK IN TIME:

CHECK OUT TIME:

DIRECTIONS

Ideas

WRITE DOWN YOUR THOUGHTS AND IDEAS FOR THE BACHELORETTE PARTY!

Ideas

WRITE DOWN YOUR THOUGHTS AND IDEAS FOR THE BACHELORETTE PARTY!

To Do + DELEGATION

NAME / TO DO	NOTES
☐	
☐	
☐	
☐	
☐	
☐	
☐	

NAME / TO DO	NOTES
☐	
☐	
☐	
☐	
☐	
☐	
☐	

NAME / TO DO	NOTES
☐	
☐	
☐	
☐	
☐	
☐	
☐	

To Do + DELEGATION

NAME / TO DO	NOTES
☐	
☐	
☐	
☐	
☐	
☐	
☐	

NAME / TO DO	NOTES
☐	
☐	
☐	
☐	
☐	
☐	

NAME / TO DO	NOTES
☐	
☐	
☐	
☐	
☐	
☐	

Shopping LIST

QTY	FOOD & DRINKS

QTY	PARTY DECOR

QTY	GIFTS

QTY	MISC

Shopping LIST

QTY	FOOD & DRINKS

QTY	PARTY DECOR

QTY	GIFTS

QTY	MISC

Bachelorette Party GUESTS

NAME & CONTACT	RSVP'D		NAME & CONTACT	RSVP'D	
	✗	✔		✗	✔
	✗	✔		✗	✔
	✗	✔		✗	✔
	✗	✔		✗	✔
	✗	✔		✗	✔
	✗	✔		✗	✔
	✗	✔		✗	✔
	✗	✔		✗	✔
	✗	✔		✗	✔
	✗	✔		✗	✔
	✗	✔		✗	✔
	✗	✔		✗	✔
	✗	✔		✗	✔
	✗	✔		✗	✔
	✗	✔		✗	✔
	✗	✔		✗	✔
	✗	✔		✗	✔
	✗	✔		✗	✔
	✗	✔		✗	✔
	✗	✔		✗	✔
	✗	✔		✗	✔
	✗	✔		✗	✔

Notes

Notes

Best Memories

JOURNAL

— ❤ —

Best Bridal Shower PICTURES

Best Bridal Shower MEMORIES

Best Bachelorette Party PICTURES

Best Bachelorette Party MEMORIES

Best Wedding Day PICTURES

Best Wedding Day MEMORIES

A Gift For My READERS!

BRIDAL SHOWER GAMES
4 PAGES | US LETTER SIZE | INSTANT PDF DOWNLOAD

DOWNLOAD YOUR FREE GAMES AT:
BeautyandHeartPlanners.com

Copyright & TERMS OF USE

Made in United States
North Haven, CT
09 October 2022

25218893R00052